7.7.06

KS3 Science
Essential SATS Practice

It's packed with lots of nasty questions — because they're
the sort you'll get in the exam.

They're organised by topic, so you can easily see the types of questions
you might get on each area of the curriculum.

Practise getting these questions right and you'll
sweat a lot less on the big day.

Contents

Published by Coordination Group Publications Ltd.

Contributors:

Stuart Barker, Martin Chester, Kate Manson, Becky May, Barry Pywell, Emma Singleton and James Wallis.

ISBN: 1-84146-241-1

Groovy website: www.cgpbooks.co.uk

With thanks to Ian Francis and Jennifer Underwood for the proofreading.
Jolly bits of clipart from CorelDRAW
Printed by Elanders Hindson, Newcastle upon Tyne

Electrical Conductors

1   A material that allows electricity to flow through it is called a **conductor**.
Metals are conductors.

(a)   Name **one** non-metal that is also a conductor.

....

(b)   (i)   What name is given to a material that does **not** allow charge to pass through it?

....

(ii)   Give **two** examples of materials that do not allow charge to pass through them.

1 ....   2 ....

(c)   Explain why electrical cables are usually made with
a metal core surrounded by a plastic cover.

....

....

....

2   Two electrical circuits are shown below.

(a)   In which circuit will the bulb **not** light, A or B? ....

(b)   Give **two** reasons for your answer to (a).

1 ....

2 ....

Electric Current

1   An electric current is the movement of charge around a circuit.

    (a) (i)   What are the moving charges that make up an electric current?

              ....

       (ii) Are these charges positive or negative?

              ....

    (b) (i)   What instrument is used to measure electric current?

              ....

       (ii) What units are used to measure electric current?

              ....

2   Both of the circuits below have current flowing through them.

    (a) Draw **one** arrow on each diagram to show which direction:

       (i) **conventional current** flows around a circuit.

       (ii) **charge** flows around a circuit.

    (b) What would happen to the current if there was a break in the circuit?

        ....

Electric Current

1 An electrical circuit can be compared to a system of water pipes.
Choose from the list below to give the electrical equivalent for each
part of a water system, and explain why they are similar.

wires   charge   current   switch   flow   battery   bulb   resistor

(a) **The** .... **is like a pump because** ....

....

(b) **The** .... **are like the pipes because** ....

....

(c) **The** .... **is like the water because** ....

....

(d) **A** .... **is like a narrow pipe because** ....

....

2 Tamar and Bennie are asked to explain what the battery
in the circuit below is doing to make the bulb light.

Tamar says "The battery supplies charge, and some of it is used in the bulb to make light."
Bennie says "The battery supplies energy and some of it becomes light in the bulb."

(a) Who is right, Tamar or Bennie?

....

(b) Explain your answer to (a).

....

....

Circuit Diagrams

1   Electrical components can be represented by symbols.

   (a) Draw the correct circuit symbol for each of the following components.

       (i)   A cell.   (ii)   A motor.

   (b) Write down the names of the components that have the following symbols.

       (i)   (ii)

       ....

   (c) Explain what the two symbols opposite show.

       1 ....

       2 ....

2   Electrical circuits can be represented by diagrams.
   Draw a circuit diagram for each of the circuits shown below.

   (a)

   (b)

   (c)

Series Circuits

1   The components in an electrical circuit can be connected in series or in parallel.

(a)   Explain what a series circuit is.

....

....

(b)   Put a tick below the diagrams that represent series circuits.

2   An inventor uses a motor and a cell to make a novelty spinning bow tie.

(a)   She then adds a buzzer in series with the motor. Will the bow tie spin
      more quickly, more slowly, or at the same speed? Explain your answer.

....

....

(b)   The bow tie suddenly stops spinning, but the buzzer is still working.
      The inventor decides the motor has been short circuited by another wire round
      the motor. Explain why a short circuit would stop the motor from working.

....

....

....

Section One — Electricity and Magnetism

Series Circuits

1   Donald has made his own set of battery-powered Christmas tree lights.
    A simplified diagram of his circuit is shown below.

(a) The reading on A_1 is 6.5 A. What will the reading on A_2 be? ....

(b) If one of the bulbs breaks, what effect will this have on the set of lights?

    ....

2   The current in a series circuit can be measured with a single ammeter.

(a) For each pair of circuits shown below, what will the ammeter read in **circuit 2**?
     Explain your answers.

     (i)

     ....

     ....

     (ii)

     ....

     ....

(b) The ammeter in the circuit below reads 16 A.
     Draw **two** different circuits that will have a current of 4 A flowing through them.

Parallel Circuits

1   The diagram below shows a parallel circuit with a bulb, motor, and four ammeters.

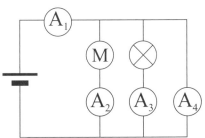

(a) Explain what is meant by a parallel circuit.

....

....

(b) (i)   Which ammeter will show how much current
          is flowing through the **whole circuit** — A_1, A_2, A_3 or A_4? ....

   (ii) Which ammeter will show how much current
          is flowing through the **bulb** — A_1, A_2, A_3 or A_4? ....

(c) (i)   Which ammeter would you expect to have the highest reading —
          A_1, A_2, A_3 or A_4? Explain your answer.

          ....

          ....

   (ii) Would you expect ammeters A_2, A_3 and A_4 to give the same readings?
          Explain your answer.

          ....

          ....

   (iii) Which ammeter would you expect to have the highest reading — A_2, A_3 or A_4?
          Explain your answer.

          ....

          ....

Parallel Circuits

1   The parallel circuit shown on the right contains
    a motor, a bulb, a buzzer and some ammeters.

    (a) Complete the table below to show all the ammeter readings.

Ammeter	1	2	3	4	5
Reading (A)	8	2	5		

    (b) The same circuit is set up, but using different components.
        It is realised that one of the new ammeters is faulty.
        Use the readings below to work out which one it is.

Ammeter	1	2	3	4	5
Reading (A)	9	3	5	2	10

    Ammeter .... is faulty.

2   The circuit below contains three bulbs and four switches.
    Complete the table to show how the bulbs can be controlled by the switches.
    The first one has been done for you.

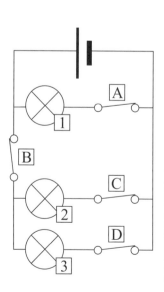

Switches				Bulbs		
A	B	C	D	1	2	3
open	closed	closed	closed	off	on	on
closed	open	closed	closed			
closed	closed	open	closed			
closed	closed	closed	open			
closed	closed	open	open			
closed	open	open	closed			
closed	closed	closed	closed			

Section One — Electricity and Magnetism

Magnets

1   Jordan is using a compass to investigate the magnetic field around a bar magnet.
    He places the compass at various positions around the magnet.

(a)   Explain what is meant by a **magnetic field**.

    ....

    ....

(b) (i)   Describe what will happen to the needle of a compass in a magnetic field.

    ....

    ....

    (ii)   Jordan has recorded his first result on the diagram below. Complete it to show
           what the compass will look like at all the other positions around the magnet.

(c)   Suggest another way, apart from using a compass,
      that Jordan can show the magnetic field around a magnet.

    ....

    ....

(d)   Complete the diagram below to show the field lines around a bar magnet.

Magnets

1   Kirsty knows that a magnet is made by putting a piece of metal in a strong magnetic field.
     She tries this out with a copper rod, then tests it by holding it near some steel paperclips.
     The paperclips are not attracted to the copper rod. She tries again using a piece of iron,
     and this time the paperclips stick to the iron bar.

(a) (i)   Why wasn't Kirsty able to make a magnet with a copper rod?

     ....

     (ii) Name **two** other metals, apart from iron, that Kirsty could use to make a magnet.

     1 ....   2 ....

(b) Because the paperclips stick to the iron, Kirsty decides she has made a magnet.

     (i)   Explain why Kirsty may be wrong to decide that the iron has become a magnet.

     ....

     ....

     (ii) Describe what Kirsty should do to test if the iron has become a magnet.

     ....

     ....

2   Peter uses one bar magnet to push another one along the tabletop, then to pull it.
     Complete the diagrams below to show all the ways the poles could have lined up.

(a) One magnet pushing the other.

     | S   N | [ ]   or   [ ] [ ]

(b) One magnet pulling the other.

     | S   N | [ ]   or   [ ] [ ]

Electromagnets

1   Rajesh is trying to make an electromagnet.

(a) With the help of a diagram, describe an electromagnet that would be simple for Rajesh to make.

    ....

    ....

(b) Give **two** ways Rajesh could increase the strength of this electromagnet.

    1 ....

    2 ....

(c) Explain why Rajesh should **not** use steel to make the core of the electromagnet.

    ....

2   The circuit used for an alarm bell is shown below. It contains an electromagnet.

arm attached to spring
hammer
bell
spring
iron core

(a) Explain how the circuit makes the bell ring continuously when the switch is closed.

    ....

    ....

    ....

(b) Give **two** reasons why an electromagnet and not a
     permanent magnet is used in the circuit.

    1 ....

    2 ....

Electromagnets

1   The design for a switch-operated electric hand drier is shown below.

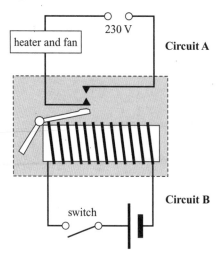

(a) (i)   What name is given to the component in the shaded box?

....

(ii) What is this component used for?

....

(b) The design contains two circuits, A and B. One can be described as an input circuit
and the other as an output circuit.

(i)   Which is which?

Circuit .... **is an input circuit. Circuit** .... **is an output circuit.**

(ii) Explain your answer to (i).

....

(c) Describe what will happen when the switch is closed.

....

....

(d) Why is it an advantage to use a design like this one for an electric hand-drier,
with two circuits rather than a switch directly connected to the mains?

....

....

Electricity and Magnetism Mini-Exam

1   Rebecca is testing different materials to see whether they will carry an electric current.

(a) (i)   What is an electric current?

    ....

    ....

    (ii) What term is used to describe materials that will carry an electric current?

    ....

Rebecca uses a cell, a buzzer and some wires to make a circuit to test the materials.

(b) To make sure the buzzer works, she connects it directly to the cell.
     Show this circuit in a circuit diagram.

Rebecca then connects various materials into the circuit
and checks whether the buzzer still works.

(c) To find out if the materials will carry an electric current, should she
     connect them in series or in parallel? Explain your answer.

    ....

    ....

(d) (i)   Name **three** substances for which the buzzer will still work.

        1 ....   2 ....

        3 ....

    (ii) Name **three** substances that will **stop** the buzzer from working.

        1 ....   2 ....

        3 ....

Electricity and Magnetism Mini-Exam

2   Ted puts a copper tube in the middle of a solenoid and connects the solenoid to a battery.
The current passing through the solenoid creates a magnetic field.

(a) (i)   What is a solenoid?

....

(ii) What has Ted made?

....

(b) (i)   Complete the diagram below to show the field lines around the solenoid.

(ii) Ted disconnects the battery from the circuit and reconnects it with its poles
the other way round. How will the magnetic field be affected by this?

....

Ted finds that the magnetic field is strong enough to pick up five paperclips.

(c) Suggest **three** things Ted could do to increase the number of paperclips picked up.

1 ....

2 ....

3 ....

Section One — Electricity and Magnetism

Electricity and Magnetism Mini-Exam

(d) (i) Suggest **two** materials that the paperclips might be made of.

1 .... 2 ....

(ii) Explain your answer to (i).

....

....

Ted adds a switch to the circuit in three different places, making three different circuits. These are shown in the diagram below.

A   **B**   **C**

(e) In which circuits is the switch connected in series? Write their letters below.

....

(f) In which circuit will **closing** the switch reduce the magnetic field?

....

(g) (i) In which circuit will little or no magnetic field be created, whether the switch is open or closed? Explain why.

....

....

....

(ii) What is this effect called?

....

Electricity and Magnetism Mini-Exam

3   Claire has bought three identical decorative lights for her new living room.
She wants to connect them so that they work on mains electricity, so that they are on the same switch, and so that if any light fails, the others will carry on working.

(a)   Complete the diagram below to show a circuit Claire could use for her new lights.

(b)   Claire also needs to add a fuse to her circuit.
This is a safety device included in all circuits connected to mains electricity.
If there is a dangerous increase in the current flowing, it melts and shuts off the current.
Should Claire connect the fuse in series or in parallel? Explain your answer.

....

....

....

4   The circuit below contains four identical bulbs. Ammeter A_1 reads 12 A.

(a)   What are the readings on the other ammeters?

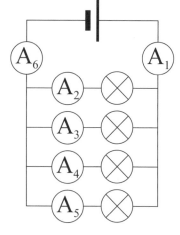

A_2 .... A_5 ....

A_3 .... A_6 ....

A_4 ....

(b)   Has any current been used up in the circuit?
Explain how you know.

....

(c)   Where does the light energy given out by the bulbs come from?

....

Speed

1   A new racing car is being tested to find its top speed by driving it along a straight track.
There are two posts on the track, 1 mile apart.

(a) During one test run, the car takes 60 seconds to move between the two posts.
What is its speed in miles/hour?

....

(b) The makers of the car have predicted that the car's top speed will be 200 miles/hour.

(i)   If the car travels at 200 miles/hour, how long will it take
to pass between the posts, in hours?

....

(ii) How long will it take in seconds?

....

(c) At a constant speed of 120 miles/hour, the car travels the whole length
of the track in 3 minutes. How long is the track? Include the unit.

....

2   Chris and Jenny both walked to the same beach,
but they took different routes.

(a) Jenny took 10 minutes to reach the beach. What speed
was she travelling at, in km/hour? Show your working.

....

....

(b) Chris walked at 4 km/hour. Did he arrive at the beach before or after Jenny?
Show your working.

....

....

Speed

1   A research scientist is investigating the properties of various liquids.
He drops a metal ball down a tube filled with one of the liquids and measures the time
taken for the ball to pass between two marks on the tube. The marks are 50 cm apart.
Some of the results are shown in the table below.

Liquid	Time taken to pass between marks	Speed
A	10 seconds	
B	2 seconds	
C	5 seconds	
D		1.0 m/s
E		2.5 m/s
F		0.4 m/s

(a) Did the ball drop more quickly through liquid A or through liquid B?

    ....

(b) What was the speed of the ball when it passed between the marks in liquid C,
in metres per second?

    ....

(c) How long did the ball take to pass between the marks in liquid D?

    ....

(d) How long would the ball take to pass through 15 m of liquid E?

    ....

(e) How far through liquid F would the ball travel in 23 seconds?

    ....

Speed

1   The triathlon is a sport that combines swimming, running and cycling in one race.
The graph below shows the speed of one athlete during a triathlon.

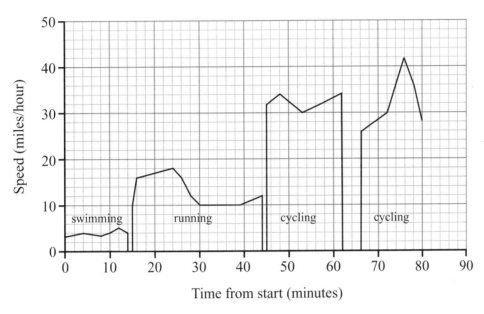

(a) How many minutes after the start of the triathlon was the athlete travelling at her fastest?

....

(b) She had to stop cycling to mend a puncture. For how long did she stop?

....

(c) The athlete ran at a constant speed from 30 minutes to 39 minutes into the race.

    (i) How fast was she running during this time?

    ....

    (ii) How far did she run during this time?

    ....

(d) The athlete's time for the race was 90 minutes. In the last 6 minutes of the race, the athlete
travelled 4.4 miles at a constant speed. Complete the **last 6 minutes** on the graph to show
this. Use the space below for your working.

....

(e) The athlete cycled for 24 miles in total. What was her **average** cycling speed?

....

Force and Movement

1   The device shown opposite is used to measure forces.
It contains a strong spring and a scale.

(a) (i)   What is the name of the device?

....

(ii) What are the units on its scale?

....

The diagram to the right shows a mass hanging from the device.
A pair of forces act on the mass, one upward and one downward.

(b) What is causing

(i)   The downward force acting on the mass?

....

(ii) The upward force acting on the mass?

....

(c) The pointer on the scale of the device is not moving.
What can you say about the forces acting on the mass?

....

2   To finish off her cheesecake, Tessa adds a layer of whipped cream and
a strawberry on top. There are two forces acting on the strawberry —
an upward force from the cream and a downward force of gravity.

What will happen if

(a) The two forces are balanced?

....

(b) The force of gravity is larger than the force from the cream?

....

Force and Movement

1 Each of the pictures below shows a situation where a force is acting on an object. Next to each one, write down the **main** overall effect of the forces on movement. Choose from the following options:

speed up   **slow down**   **change direction**   **turn**   **change shape**

(a) A cyclist starts pedalling.

(b) The parachute suddenly opens.

....

(c) Cricketer hits a ball.

....

....

2 The diagrams below show a mass hanging from an **elastic** bungee rope after it has been dropped. The force of gravity acts downwards on the mass, and a force from the rope acts upwards. The upward force varies depending on the length of the rope.

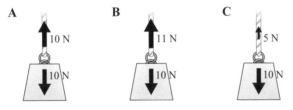

A   10 N   10 N

B   11 N   10 N

C   5 N   10 N

(a) Which diagram — A, B or C — shows the mass when it is

(i) speeding up on the way down? ....

(ii) speeding up on the way up?   ....

(iii) not moving?   ....

(b) Which diagram shows the mass the longest time after it has been dropped? Explain your answer.

....

....

(c) The weight of the mass is a force that acts on the rope. What effect does this force have on **the rope**?

....

Air Resistance and Friction

1 A skydiver falling through the air has opposing forces acting
   on him due to gravity and air resistance.

(a) What is air resistance?

....

(b) (i) Describe how the force of air resistance affects the skydiver at the instant he
          steps out of the plane, before he starts to fall. Explain your answer.

....

....

(ii) The skydiver starts to fall more and more quickly.
      What happens to the air resistance acting on him?

....

(c) (i) What happens to air resistance when the skydiver's parachute opens?

....

(ii) Explain why the skydiver falls at a steady speed with the parachute open.

....

....

(d) Write down the letters of the diagrams and labels below in the correct order in the table.

	Diagram	Label
1		
2		
3		
4		
5		

A Steady speed

B Losing speed

C Rapidly gaining speed

D Weight equal to reaction
   force from ground

E Gradually gaining speed

V

air resistance

weight

W

X

Y

Z

Section Two — Forces and Motion

Air Resistance and Friction

1   Two motorbikes are shown below.

A   B

(a)   Describe **two** ways in which friction is an **advantage** when riding a motorbike.

1   ....

....

2   ....

....

(b)   Describe **two** ways in which friction is a **disadvantage** when riding a motorbike.

1   ....

....

2   ....

....

The motorbikes above have the same mass and the same engine power.

(c)   Which do you think will have the higher top speed, A or B? Explain your answer.

....

....

(d)   If the motorbikes are travelling at the same speed, suggest
which one will use fuel more quickly. Explain your answer.

....

....

Force and Rotation

1   Toby is using a lever to raise a barrel of water.

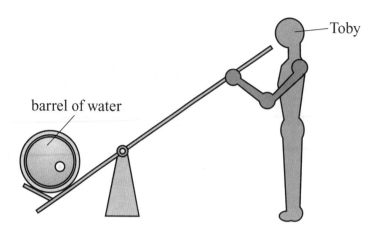

barrel of water

Toby

(a) (i) Add **two** arrows to the diagram above to show the **direction** and the **size**
(i.e. which force is bigger) of the forces exerted by Toby and by the barrel.
Label them **effort force** and **load**.

(ii) Label the diagram to show where the **pivot** is.

(b) What is a pivot?

....

(c) Using the labelled diagram, explain why a lever can be called a machine.

....

....

....

(d) (i) How can Toby reduce the effort he has to put in to lift the barrel,
without changing the lever he is using?

....

(ii) Explain your answer to (i).

....

....

Force and Rotation

1 There are many examples of levers in everyday life.

(a) Draw and label arrows to show the direction of the effort force and load,
plus the pivot, in each picture below.

(i)

(ii)

nutcracker & walnut

(iii)

(b) A tool-making company has designed two different wirecutters, shown below.

A

B

(i) Which is the better design, A or B? ....

(ii) Give **two** reasons for your answer to (i).

1 ....

2 ....

2 Gordon and Barry are equally matched at
arm wrestling — their hands are not moving.

(a) Draw and label two arrows on the picture opposite
to show the effort force and load for **Barry**.
Both the size and the direction of the forces
should be shown.

(b) Compared to the other levers on this page,
what is different about the arm as a lever?

....

....

Moments

1   The diagram below shows a set of scales used to measure rice.
     Rice is placed in the dish, and the mass is moved along the arm until the scales balance.

(a)   The weight of the rice and of the mass create turning forces about the pivot.

   (i)   What name is given to a turning force about a pivot?

      ....

   (ii)   What are the units used to measure such a turning force?

      ....

A bag of rice with weight 10 N is placed in the dish.

(b)   What turning force will act about the pivot? Show your working and give the units.

   ....

(c)   What distance from the pivot must the mass be placed to balance the scales?
      Show your working and give the units.

   ....

   ....

(d)   What weight of rice will balance the scales if the mass is 10 cm from the pivot?
      Show your working and give the units.

   ....

   ....

   ....

Moments

1   Diagram A below shows the structure of Jason's arm. The arm muscles attached
to the forearm exert a force that can make the forearm pivot around the elbow.
Diagram B is a simplified diagram showing the moments that act about Jason's
elbow when he holds an object in his hand.

A

B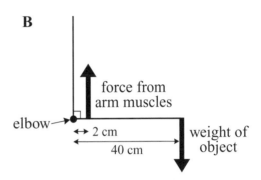

(a)   Jason's arm muscles exert a force at 2 cm from the elbow. The largest force that they
can exert is 4000 N. What moment will this give about the elbow, in Newton metres?

....

....

(b)   (i)   Will the maximum weight that Jason can hold steady in his hand
be smaller or larger than 4000 N? Explain your answer.

....

....

....

(ii)   Calculate the maximum weight that Jason will be able to support in his hand.

....

....

(iii) Jason tries to hold a 220 N weight in his hand. Suggest what will happen.

....

....

Moments

1   Bomb-disposal experts often need to open up a bomb to defuse it.
    A remote-controlled 'spanner' can be used to unscrew parts of the bomb at a safe distance.
    This uses rockets to supply the turning force.

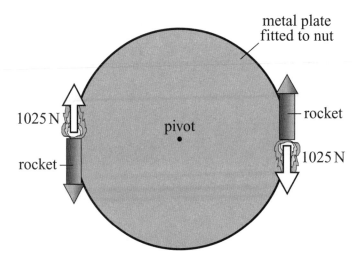

The 'spanner' in the diagram above is set up so that each rocket is 0.1 m from the pivot.
It is being used to unscrew a nut on a Second World War bomb.

(a) (i)   At the first attempt to unscrew the nut, one of the rockets fails to fire.
           What is the moment created by the other rocket?
           Show your working and give the units.

           ....

     (ii) At the second attempt, both rockets fire. What is the moment created?
           Show your working and give the units.

           ....

(b) The nut is not loosened even when both rockets fire. The experts decide to increase
     the moment to 820 Nm by fixing more rockets to the spanner.

     (i)   How many rockets are needed to produce this moment?
           (Each rocket exerts a force of 1025 Nm at a distance of 0.1 m from the pivot.)

           ....

           ....

     (ii) How could the bomb-disposal experts increase
           the moment without using more rockets?

           ....

Pressure

1 Mairi hammers a nail into a wall with a force of 12 N.

(a) The point of the nail has an area of 0.1 cm².
What pressure is exerted by the hammer on the point of the nail

(i) in N/cm²? Show your working.

....

(ii) in N/m²? Show your working.

....

(iii) in Pascals?

....

(b) Mairi misses the nail and hits the wall with the hammer.
Explain why the hammer doesn't penetrate the wall, even though the nail does.

....

....

....

2 Max stands with both feet on the floor.
Each foot exerts a pressure of 12 000 Pa on the floor.

(a) What will the pressure on the floor be if Max lifts one foot off the floor?
Explain your answer.

....

....

(b) The area of contact between the soles of Max's feet (with both feet on the floor) and
the floor is 0.06 m². What does Max weigh? Show your working and give the units.

....

....

Pressure

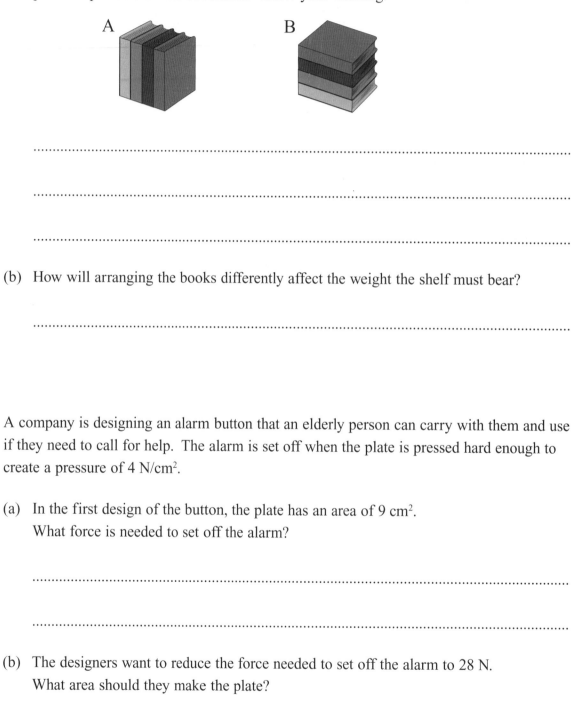

1   Isobel is arranging a set of four books on her new bookshelves.
     Each book has the dimensions shown opposite and weighs 27 N.

20 cm

3 cm

27 cm

(a) Which of the two ways of arranging the books shown below will
     put least pressure on the bookshelf? Show your working.

     A

     B

     ....

     ....

     ....

(b) How will arranging the books differently affect the weight the shelf must bear?

     ....

2   A company is designing an alarm button that an elderly person can carry with them and use
     if they need to call for help. The alarm is set off when the plate is pressed hard enough to
     create a pressure of 4 N/cm^2.

(a) In the first design of the button, the plate has an area of 9 cm^2.
     What force is needed to set off the alarm?

     ....

     ....

(b) The designers want to reduce the force needed to set off the alarm to 28 N.
     What area should they make the plate?

     ....

     ....

Pressure

1. Anne has bought a statue for her garden, but the ground where she wants to put it is soft. She estimates that if the pressure of the statue on the ground goes over 4000 Pa it will sink.

    (a) The statue weighs 450 N and has an area of contact with the ground of 0.06 m². Anne thinks it will sink.
    Is she correct? Show your working.

    ....

    ....

    (b) She decides to make a base for the statue out of concrete.
    Explain how adding a base can reduce the pressure of the statue on the ground.

    ....

    ....

    (c) The base has an area of 0.16 m².
    What is the maximum weight Anne can make the base?

    ....

    ....

2. Alan is building a house. The house exerts a force of 240 000 N on the foundations. The foundations spread this load over an area of 8 m².

    (a) What is the pressure on the foundations?

    ....

    (b) Building laws say that the pressure on the foundations should be not more than 32 000 Pa. How much smaller could Alan have made the area of the foundations without breaking the building laws?

    ....

    ....

Forces and Motion Mini-Exam

1   The picture opposite shows a reclining bicycle.
Unlike a standard bicycle, the pedals are in front of the rider,
who has to lie back in the seat to reach them.

Various forces act against the bicycle when it moves along,
such as air resistance and the resistance
of the bicycle's parts to movement.

(a) (i)   What type of force are all the forces acting against
           the movement of the bicycle examples of?

....

     (ii) Give **one** way that this type of force is useful to the bicycle's rider.

....

(b) Suggest why the reclining bicycle has a higher top speed than most standard bicycles.

....

At a constant speed, the bicycle takes 12.5 s to travel between two poles 0.15 km apart.
During this time, the force acting against the movement of the bicycle is 120 N.

(c) What is the speed of the bicycle? Show your working and give the units.

....

(d) (i)   What is the forward force produced by the rider? Explain how you know.

....

....

     (ii) Explain in terms of forces what happens to the movement
           of the bicycle if the rider reduces the forward force.

....

....

....

Forces and Motion Mini-Exam

2   A simplified diagram of a car's braking system is shown below. The force of the driver's foot on the brake pedal is transferred to the brake pad by a liquid called brake fluid. Force Y is the force of the brake pad on the wheel.

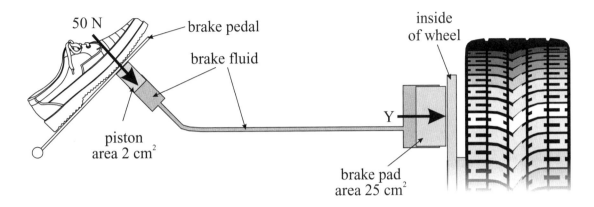

(a)   In the diagram above, the driver applies a force of 50 N to the brake pedal.

(i)   What is the pressure of the piston on the brake fluid, in N/cm²?
Show your working.

....

....

(ii)   The pressure of the piston on the brake fluid is the same as the pressure of the brake fluid on the brake pad. Calculate force Y, giving the correct units.

....

....

(b)   (i)   On a hill, the brake pad must produce a braking force of at least 450 N to stop the car from rolling backwards. The perpendicular distance from the brake pad to the centre of the wheel is 0.14 m. What is the smallest moment that will hold the car still? Show your working and give the units.

....

(ii)   On another hill, a moment of at least 35 Nm is needed to keep the car still. What is the minimum braking force that the brake pad must produce? Show your working and give the units.

....

Forces and Motion Mini-Exam

3   A door is fitted with a closing device to stop the wind blowing it open.
In the diagram below, force W is the force of the wind against the door,
and force C is the force exerted by the closing device. The area of the door is 1.6 m².

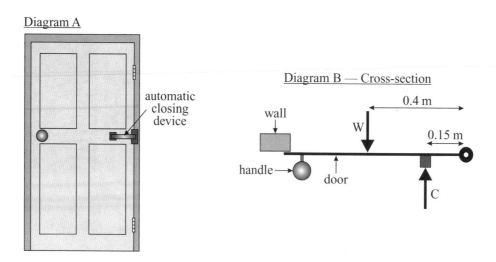

Diagram A

Diagram B — Cross-section

(a) The door acts as a lever.

   (i)   Label the **pivot** on diagram B.

   (ii) Which of the two forces is the **effort force** and which is the **load**?

   Force W is the ....

   Force C is the ....

(b) A wind blowing at 5 m/s exerts a pressure of 20 Pa on the door.

   (i)   What is the force of the wind against the door? Show your working.

   ....

   (ii) The force of the wind acts at a perpendicular distance of 0.4 m from the pivot.
         Calculate the moment of the force about the pivot.

   ....

   (iii) The moment produced by the closing device about the pivot is 10 Nm.
         Will the door be blown open by the wind? Explain your answer.

   ....

   ....

   ....

Forces and Motion Mini-Exam

Jessica is pulling on the door so that it stays partly open.
In the diagram below, force C is the force exerted by the closing device and
force J is the force exerted by Jessica pulling on the door handle.

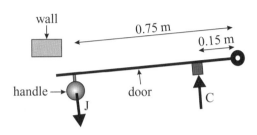

(c) Force C is 10 N. What is the moment of force C about the pivot?
Show your working.

....

(d) (i) What is the moment of force J about the pivot? Explain how you know.

....

(ii) Calculate the value of force J, in newtons.

....

(e) Explain the relationship between force J and force C.

....

....

(f) What will happen to the movement of the door if force J

(i) **increases?** ....

(ii) **decreases?** ....

(g) The makers of the closing device decide to change the design to produce
a larger moment about the pivot. Describe **two** ways they could do this.

1 ....

2 ....

Section Three — Light and Sound

Properties of Light

1   Charmaine enters a darkened room, and switches on a table lamp.
There is a mug on the table in front of her.

(a) (i) Draw a ray of light on the diagram above to show how
Charmaine is able to see the light bulb in the table lamp.

(ii) Using the diagram you completed in (i),
explain how Charmaine is able to see the light bulb.

....

....

(iii) Name **two** other objects (not visible in the diagram) that Charmaine
would be able to see in the same way.

1 ....   2 ....

(b) (i) Draw a ray of light on the diagram above to show how
Charmaine is able to see the mug on the table.

(ii) Name **two** other objects (not visible in the diagram) that Charmaine
would be able to see in the same way.

1 ....   2 ....

(iii) Why wouldn't Charmaine be able to see the mug without switching on the lamp?

....

....

Properties of Light

1   The pinhole camera in the diagram below is used to trace an image of a tree.

tracing
paper screen   box

pinhole

(a)   Draw lines to show how the image of the tree is formed on the tracing paper screen.

(b)   Explain why the image of the tree appears upside down.

....

....

2   Arif and Pritti are watching a firework display at their local park.

(a)   The display takes place at night, and there are very few lights in the park.

(i)   Explain why Arif and Pritti can see the fireworks explode even though it is dark.

....

(ii)   Suggest how their view of the fireworks would be affected
if there were more lights in the park. Explain your answer.

....

....

(b)   They hear the explosions of the fireworks a short time after they see them,
and Arif hears the explosions about a second after Pritti does.

(i)   Who is watching the display from further away, Arif or Pritti?
Explain how you know.

....

(ii)   Arif and Pritti see the fireworks explode at the same time. Using your
answer to (i), suggest how the speed of light compares to the speed of sound.

....

....

Reflection

1   The diagram below shows a ray of light hitting a mirror.

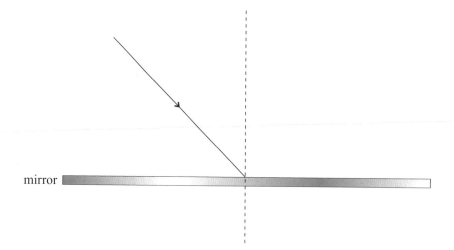

(a)   Label the diagram with the correct **names** for the following.

(i)   The ray of light travelling to the mirror.   (ii)   The dotted line.

(b)   On the diagram, draw

(i)   The angle of incidence, **i**.

(ii)   The reflected light ray.

(iii)   The angle of reflection, **r**.

(c)   The diagram above is an example of the law of reflection.

(i)   What is the law of reflection?

....

....

(ii)   Explain why the light falling on a mirror obeys the law of reflection.

....

....

(iii)   Describe a situation where the light falling on an object
does not obey the law of reflection.

....

....

Reflection

1 Claire is using a periscope to see Johan, who is standing on the other side of the wall.

(a) What property of light means that Claire is not able to see Johan without the periscope?

....

(b) Complete the diagram above, by

(i) drawing the two mirrors in Claire's periscope.

(ii) drawing a ray of light to show how the periscope allows Claire to see Johan.

2 A sheet of paper will reflect much more light than a sheet of glass.

(a) (i) Suggest what will happen to the light falling on a sheet of glass that is not reflected.

....

(ii) Explain why a sheet of glass gives a clear reflection.

....

....

(b) (i) What term is used to describe the type of reflection that happens when light hits a sheet of paper?

....

(ii) Explain why a sheet of paper does not give a clear reflection.

....

....

Reflection

1   Mirrors have been used in theatres to make 'ghosts' appear on stage.
    The diagram below shows how this can be done.

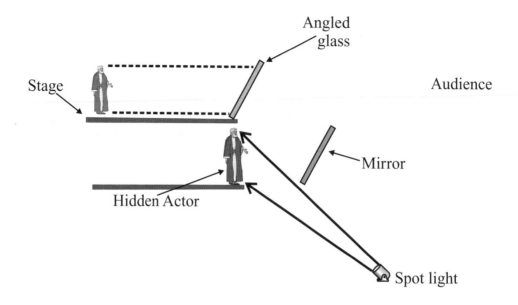

(a) Complete the two rays of light in the diagram to show
     how the image of the ghost reaches the audience.

(b) The ghost can be made to disappear. Suggest how this is done.

     ....

(c) Explain why the sheet of angled glass on the stage
     can be described as a **two-way mirror**.

     ....

     ....

     ....

(d) Describe **three** other uses for mirrors.

     1 ....

     2 ....

     3 ....

Refraction

1   Light rays can be bent when they pass from one medium to another.

(a) (i)   All the media (substances) that light can pass between
            have one property in common. What is it?

....

     (ii) What name is given to the bending of light when it passes between media?

....

(b) Explain why light is bent when it passes from one medium to another.

....

....

....

(c) Complete the diagrams below to show the path taken by a ray of light
     as it passes from air into the glass blocks and back into air.

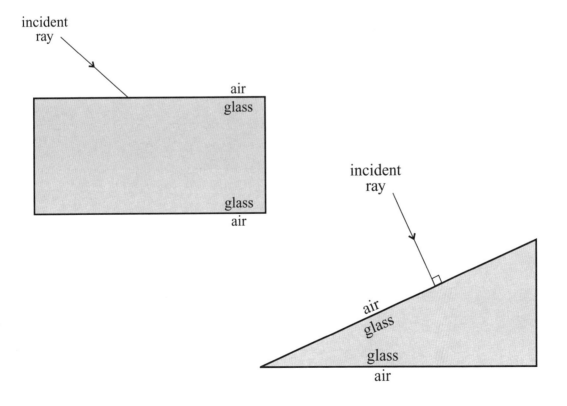

Refraction

1   Lesley is investigating how much light bends when it passes between different media.
She sets up two experiments. In the first one, she shines a ray of light so that it travels
from air into water. In the second one, the ray travels from air into glass.

   (a) Name **one** thing that Lesley should keep the same in both
        experiments so that she can compare the results.

   ....

   The diagram below shows Lesley's results.

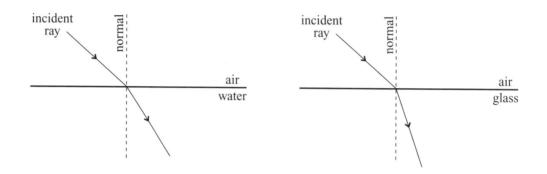

   (b) Does light travel more quickly through **water** or **glass**? Explain your answer.

   ....

   ....

   ....

   (c) Complete the diagram below to show how you would expect
        light to bend as it travels from **water** to **glass**.

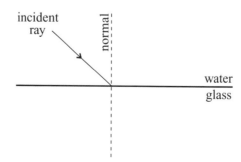

Refraction

1   Tariq asks Drew to stand at a particular spot in the room, and look at a bowl on the table in front of him. There is a coin in the bowl, but Drew can't see it from where he's standing. Tariq then carefully pours some water into the bowl, and the coin 'appears'.

(a)   What property of the material the bowl is made out of
means that Drew can't see the coin until Tariq pours the water in?

....

In the diagram below, the dotted lines show how Drew sees the coin
as if the light rays were travelling in a straight line.

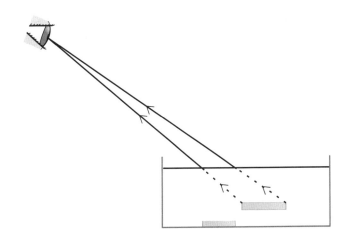

(b)   Complete the diagram to show the path the light rays actually take.

(c)   Use the completed diagram to answer the following questions.

   (i)   Should a fisherman on a riverbank aim to cast his bait
   beyond, before or straight at the place he sees a fish?

   ....

   (ii)   Explain why, when you are standing on the side of a
   swimming pool, it is always deeper than it looks.

   ....

   ....

   ....

   ....

Colour

1   When white light shines on a glass prism it bends and is split up into different colours.
     In the diagram below, a rainbow pattern appears on the screen.

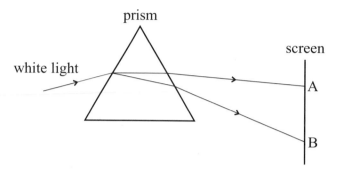

(a) What term is used to describe

    (i)   The rainbow pattern on the screen?

    ....

    (ii) The splitting of light into different colours?

    ....

(b) (i)   Name the colour that appears at A on the screen.

    ....

    (ii) Name the colour that appears at B on the screen.

    ....

    (iii) Explain why the different colours split up when white light is shone on a prism.

    ....

    ....

    ....

(c) A rainbow sometimes forms when it rains. Explain how this happens.

    ....

    ....

    ....

Colour

1   Eric sets up the four experiments shown below to investigate how different colours of
    filters and light can change the way objects look. He uses a poppy from his garden.
    In daylight it has a red flower and green leaves. He also uses a magenta filter,
    which absorbs all colours of light except red and blue and a blue filter,
    which absorbs all colours of light except blue.

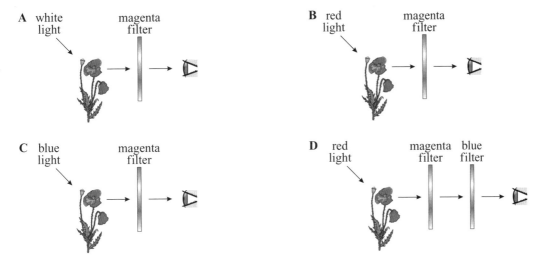

(a) For each experiment, say what colour the poppy **flower** will appear to be
     when Eric looks at it through the filter, and explain your answer.

A   **Colour** .... **Explanation** ....

....

B   **Colour** .... **Explanation** ....

....

C   **Colour** .... **Explanation** ....

....

D   **Colour** .... **Explanation** ....

....

(b) What colour will the poppy's **leaves** appear in all the experiments?
     Explain your answer.

....

....

Section Three — Light and Sound

46

Sound

1   Joel and Zach are astronauts. They are working on the outside of a new space station, which means they have to work in the vacuum of space.

(a)   Explain why Joel and Zach can see each other but must use radios to hear each other.

....

....

(b)   Joel's radio fails. Describe how the sound of Zak's voice is able to reach Joel if they put their helmets together so that they touch.

....

....

2   Yasmin stands at the mouth of a cave and claps her hands. She hears the sound twice, first at the time she claps her hands and then again a few moments later.

(a)   (i)   What term is used to describe the sound when Yasmin hears it the second time?

....

(ii)   What happened to the sound that means she hears it a second time?

....

(b)   Explain why there is a delay before Yasmin hears the sound for the second time.

....

(c)   The second time Yasmin hears the sound it is fainter. Suggest why.

....

(d)   Yasmin knows that sound travels at about 300 m/s.
Suggest how she could use this information to estimate the size of the cave.

....

....

Section Three — Light and Sound

Sound

1   Ivan is using an oscilloscope connected to a microphone to investigate sounds.
He plays three notes on his violin, and obtains traces of the sound waves he makes.
The traces are shown below. They all have the same amplitude.

G sharp

C natural

E flat

(a) Explain what is meant by the amplitude of a wave.

....

(b) All the notes Ivan plays have a different pitch. In what way do they sound similar?

....

(c) Ivan plays another note, and this time the trace has a smaller amplitude.
Describe **two** changes in the experiment that could have made the amplitude smaller.

1 ....

2 ....

2   Oscilloscope traces were obtained for the following sounds
using the same oscilloscope settings.

quiet talking

a rock band

road traffic

(a) (i)   Which of the sounds was loudest? Explain how you know.

....

....

(ii) Explain why this sound was loudest.

....

(b) On the oscilloscope screen on the right, draw how you would
expect the trace for the sound of a whisper to look.

Sound

1   The oscilloscope traces for sound waves with different frequencies are shown below.

      a car engine   a scream   a dentist's drill   a road drill

(a) (i)   What is meant by the frequency of a wave?

....

(ii)   Describe the relationship between frequency and the way a noise sounds.

....

(b) Write the noises shown in the diagram above in order of frequency, lowest first.

1 ....   2 ....

3 ....   4 ....

2   Abdul has a new mobile phone, with four different ring tones to choose from.
The oscilloscope traces for the ring tones are shown below.

(a) Which ring tone has three notes in it? Explain how you know.

....

(b) Which ring tone contains the lowest note? ....

(c) Abdul decides to program the phone with his own ring tone.
It has two notes. The first note is the same as in A above.
The second note is twice the frequency of the first.
On the oscilloscope screen opposite, draw what the trace
for Abdul's ring tone might look like.

Hearing

1 Julie whispers to Heather during a lesson.

(a) Label the following parts of Heather's ear on the diagram above.

semi-circular canals   **ear drum**   **cochlea**

ear bones   **Eustachian tube**   **auditory nerve**

(b) When Julie whispers, the vocal cords in her throat vibrate.
Use the diagram to help you describe what happens to these
vibrations so that Heather hears them as the sound of Julie's whisper.

....

....

....

....

(c) The table opposite shows the
loudness of some sounds.

Sound	Loudness (dB)
Quietest sound it is possible to hear	1
Quiet talking	40
A busy classroom	70

(i) What does dB stand for?

....

(ii) Use the table to estimate the loudness of Julie's whisper.

....

(iii) The teacher is standing next to Julie.
Suggest why Heather hears Julie's whisper but the teacher does not.

....

....

Hearing

1   Matthew is carrying out an experiment to find the audible range of pitch for four people.
He connects a signal generator to a loudspeaker. Each person being tested sits with their
back to the loudspeaker and raises their hand every time they hear a sound from it.

(a)   Briefly describe what Matthew should do
to find the audible range of pitch for each person.

....

....

....

(b)   Give **two** things that should be kept the same for each person
to make sure that the results can be compared.

1   ....

2   ....

Matthew's results are shown opposite.

(c)   Complete the graph by writing in
the correct unit for frequency.

(d)   Which person

(i)   Has the largest audible range?

....

(ii)   Is likely to be the oldest?

....

(iii)   Is likely to be the youngest?

....

(e)   Write down **two** possible causes of a smaller audible range of pitch, apart from age.

1   ....

2   ....

Light and Sound Mini-Exam

1 Tom's new clock has four different alarm sounds.
The patterns made by the sound waves on an oscilloscope screen are shown below.

(a) Write the letters of the alarm sounds
in the correct box in the table opposite.

(b) Which of the sound waves carry the same energy?

.... **and** ....

.... **and** ....

	60 dB	80 dB
8000 Hz		
10 000 Hz		

2 In one of the first experiments used to measure the speed of sound,
a man called William Derham watched a cannon being fired 12 miles away.
He started a timer when he saw the flash from the cannon,
and stopped it when he heard the explosion.

(a) Explain why the time between seeing the flash and hearing the explosion was an
accurate measure of the time the sound took to reach William Derham.

....

....

(b) William Derham found that changes in wind direction
could change the time he recorded.

(i) Suggest why changes in wind direction could change
the time it took William Derham to hear the explosion.

....

....

(ii) Suggest what he did to allow for this variation in his results.

....

....

Light and Sound Mini-Exam

3   **Lasers** produce very bright light.
A laser beam contains only one colour of light and travels in a very precise straight line.

The diagram below shows a laser beam shining onto glass.
Most of the light enters the glass, but some is reflected.

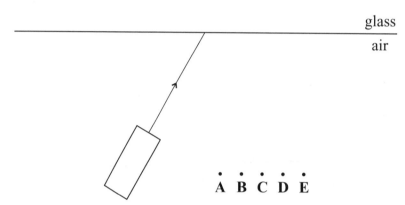

(a)   What property of the glass means that light can travel through it?

....

(b)   (i)   What will happen to the light that enters the glass?

....

(ii)   Explain why this happens.

....

....

....

(iii)   Draw a ray of light on the diagram to show
the path taken by the light that enters the glass.

(c)   Which of the points **A** to **E** on the diagram will the **reflected** light pass through?
Explain how you know.

....

....

Light and Sound Mini-Exam

(d) Describe what will happen to the light if the glass is replaced with

(i) A mirror.

....

(ii) A sheet of white paper.

....

In the diagram below, a beam of green laser light travels through a glass prism
and onto a white screen, where it appears as a spot of green light.

glass
prism

white
screen

green light

(e) (i) Describe what you would see if the screen was green. Explain your answer.

....

....

(ii) Describe what you would see if the screen was red. Explain your answer.

....

....

(f) The laser light is replaced with white light.

(i) What will appear on the screen? Explain why.

....

....

(ii) A blue filter is placed between the prism and the screen.
     What will appear on the screen? Explain why.

....

....

Light and Sound Mini-Exam

4   A fishing boat is equipped with an **echo sounder** to help it find shoals of fish.
The echo sounder sends pulses of high frequency sound into the ocean and detects any
pulses that bounce back from objects underwater.

During one fishing trip, the boat sends out pulses of sound at three different locations.
At the first two locations, the pulses come back after 3 s.
At the third location, the pulse comes back after 1 s, then again after 3 s.
The skipper decides to cast his nets at the third location.

(a) (i)   Suggest what object causes the pulse to return to the boat after 3 s.

....

(ii) Explain the skipper's decision to cast his nets at the third location.

....

....

Below are three oscilloscope traces of pulses from the echo sounder.

(b) Which trace best represents the pulse

(i)   When it is first sent out? ....

(ii)   When it comes back after 1 s? ....

(iii) When it comes back after 3 s? ....

(c) Explain your answer to (b).

....

(d) The sound produced by the echo sounder has a large amplitude and a frequency well
over 20 000 Hz. Explain why this is not a problem for fishermen, but some scientists
are concerned about the effect on dolphins.

....

....

Day and Night

1 In the diagram opposite, Birmingham in England is labelled B, and Kuala Lumpur in Malaysia is labelled KL.

(a) Use the diagram to explain how day time changes to night time.

....

....

(b) Write **B** next to the statement that **best describes** the time of day in Birmingham, and **KL** next to the statement that **best describes** the time of day in Kuala Lumpur.

It is midday. ....   The Sun has just set. ....

It is midnight. ....   The Sun will rise soon. ....

2 The diagram shows the path of the Sun across the sky for one day in spring.

(a) (i) Mark the position of the Sun at midday with a cross.

(ii) Draw the path of the Sun across the sky for one day in winter.
Label the path **winter**, and mark the position of the Sun at midday with a cross.

(iii) Draw the path of the Sun across the sky for one day in summer.
Label the path **summer**, and mark the position of the Sun at midday with a cross.

(b) Are shadows at midday longest during **spring**, **summer** or **winter**? Explain your answer.

....

....

(c) Tick the **most accurate** of the following statements about the Sun.

It moves from east to west. ☐   It appears to move from west to east. ☐

It moves from west to east. ☐   It appears to move from east to west. ☐

Seasons

1   The diagrams below show the Earth at different times in a year.

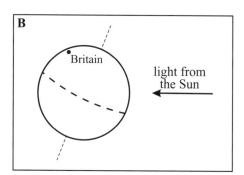

(a) (i)   What is a year?

....

(ii) Explain why every fourth year is a leap year.

....

....

The Earth's tilt causes the seasons.

(b) Which diagram, **A** or **B**, shows Britain when it is

(i)   summer?   ....

(ii) winter?   ....

(c) What **two** things are changed by the Earth's tilt, causing the seasons?

1 ....

2 ....

(d) Explain why it is summer in the southern hemisphere
     when it is winter in the northern hemisphere.

....

....

Satellites

1 The Earth has only one moon.

(a) Moons are natural satellites. Explain what is meant by this statement.

....

....

(b) Even though it has no light of its own, the Moon is usually
the brightest object in the night sky. Explain why.

....

The diagram below shows the Moon at different points in its orbit.

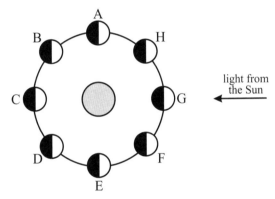

(c) Explain why the Moon appears to change shape as it orbits the Earth.

....

....

(d) Use the information below to answer the questions that follow.

When the whole face of the Moon can be seen, it is called a **Full** Moon.
When the face of the Moon is more than half but less
than fully visible, it is called a **gibbous** Moon.
When the face of the Moon is less than half visible, it is called a **crescent** Moon.
When the Moon cannot be seen at all, it is called a **New** Moon.

At which of the points **A** to **H** in the diagram above will the Moon be

(i) Full? ....

(ii) Gibbous? ....

(iii) Crescent? ....

(iv) New? ....

58

Gravity

1   The diagrams on the right show Jupiter and
    one of its forty-seven known moons,
    and the Earth and its only moon.

    (a) (i)   What is the name of the force that keeps
              the moons in orbit around the planets?

                                                            Not to scale

         ....

         (ii) Draw an arrow on each of the diagrams to show the direction of the
              force that keeps the moons in orbit around the planets.

    (b) Io and the Moon have about the same mass, but Jupiter has a **much** larger mass than
        the Earth. Will the force that keeps Io in orbit be **larger** than, **the same** as or **smaller**
        than the force that keeps the Moon in orbit around the Earth? Explain your answer.

        ....

        ....

    (c) The Moon's orbit is circular. Suggest why Jupiter's moons **don't** tend to have circular orbits.

        ....

2   The diagram shows a satellite orbiting a planet.
    It has released a probe.

    (a) The force of gravity between the planet and the satellite
        keeps the satellite in orbit. What happened to the size of this
        force after the probe was released? Explain your answer.

        ....

        ....

    (b) A force of gravity between the planet and the probe is pulling the probe down
        towards the surface. What will happen to the size of this force as the
        probe gets nearer to the surface? Explain your answer.

        ....

        ....

Section Four — The Earth and Beyond

Artificial Satellites

1 The diagram below shows a communications satellite.
Stations on the ground transmit and receive signals from the satellite.

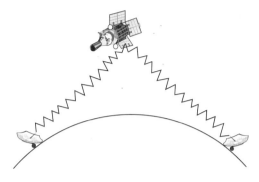

(a) Using the diagram, suggest why a signal is not sent directly between stations.

....

....

(b) The satellite is **geostationary**. It stays above the same place on the
Earth's surface, even though it is orbiting the Earth continually.

   (i) Suggest how the satellite stays above the same place on the Earth's surface.

   ....

   ....

   (ii) How long will the satellite take to complete one orbit?

   ....

(c) Describe **three** other uses of artificial satellites, apart from communications.

   1 ....

   ....

   2 ....

   ....

   3 ....

   ....

The Solar System

1   All the planets in the Solar System are visible from Earth. Mercury is between the Earth
    and the Sun. Venus is the brightest object in the sky apart from the Sun and the Moon,
    but Mercury is the most difficult to see.

    (a)   What is a planet?

    ....

    (b)   Explain why the planets in the Solar System are visible from Earth,
          even though they don't give out light.

    ....

    (c)   Suggest **one** reason for Venus's brightness.

    ....

    (d)   Suggest why Mercury is the most difficult planet to see.

    ....

2   Below is a simplified diagram of the orbits of Venus, Earth, Mars and Jupiter,
    and a table showing their orbit times to the nearest half year.

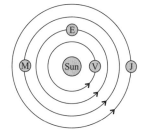

Planet	Orbit time (Earth years)
Venus	0.5
Earth	1.0
Mars	2.0
Jupiter	12.0

    (a)   On the diagram, mark the approximate position of each planet
          in six Earth months' time with a cross.

    (b)   Describe the relationship between a planet's distance from the Sun and its orbit time.

    ....

    (c)   Give **one** way in which the orbits shown in the diagram are simplified.

    ....

The Solar System

1   The table on the right contains information about
the **planets** in our Solar System.

Planet	Relative size	Relative mass
Earth	1.0	1.0
Jupiter	11.0	318.0
Mars	0.5	0.1
Mercury	0.4	0.05
Neptune	3.8	17.0
Pluto	0.2	0.003
Saturn	9.4	95.0
Uranus	4.0	15.0
Venus	0.9	0.8

(a)   What is meant by the word **relative** in the table?

....

....

....

....

(b)   In both **size** and **mass**, which of the planets is

(i)   largest?   ....

(ii)   smallest?   ....

(iii) most like Earth?   ....

(c)   (i)   Which planet is the third largest in **size**?

....

(ii)   Which planet is the third largest in **mass**?

....

(iii) Explain the difference between the **size** and the **mass** of a planet.

....

....

(d)   Explain why the Sun is not included in the table.

....

....

(e)   Name **two** other objects in the Solar System that do not appear in the table.

1 ....   2 ....

Beyond the Solar System

1   It was not until last century that astronomers began to discover galaxies other than ours.
     Planets outside our Solar System have been found only in the last few years.

(a) Write down the following objects in order of size, smallest first.

     the Sun   Solar System   Universe   planet Earth   galaxy

     ....   **smallest**

     ....

     ....

     ....

     ....   **largest**

(b) (i)   What is a galaxy?

          ....

     (ii) What name is given to our own galaxy?

          ....

     (iii) Describe what a galaxy other than our own looks like from Earth.

          ....

(c) Suggest **two** reasons why planets orbiting stars other than
     the Sun were not discovered until recently.

     1 ....

        ....

     2 ....

        ....

The Earth and Beyond Mini-Exam

1 Sanjay took a photo at night by leaving the shutter of his
camera open for about a few hours.
The diagram on the right shows the picture he got.

(a) What causes the stars in Sanjay's photo to look like
they are spinning around the night sky?

....

(b) One star in the photo doesn't seem to move.

(i) What is this star called?

....

(ii) Why doesn't the star appear to move?

....

2 The diagram on the right shows two artificial satellites
in orbit around the Earth. One satellite orbits round the
poles and the other orbits round the equator.

(a) One satellite has an orbit of 2 hours, and the other 24 hours.
If both satellites are travelling at the same speed, which satellite is
more likely to take 24 hours to complete an orbit — **A** or **B**? Explain your answer.

....

....

(b) One satellite monitors the weather and the other relays a TV signal.
Suggest which is which? Give a reason for your answers.

Satellite .... **is likely to be the weather satellite because** ....

....

Satellite .... **is likely to be the television satellite because** ....

....

The Earth and Beyond Mini-Exam

3　The position of Earth at various points in its orbit around the Sun is shown in the diagram below. Some of the stars in the constellation Orion are also shown. Note that the diagram is not to scale — Orion is **very** far from our Solar System.

Orion

(a)　How long does the Earth take to complete one orbit, in days? Answer as accurately as you can.

....

(b)　(i)　What is the Sun?

....

　　　(ii)　Describe **two** effects the Sun has on planet Earth.

　　　　1 ....

　　　　2 ....

(c)　The height the Sun reaches in Earth's sky changes depending on the position of the Earth in its orbit.

　　　(i)　What causes the Sun to 'move' across Earth's sky once every 24 hours?

....

....

　　　(ii)　At which point in the Earth's orbit will the Sun appear lowest in the sky in the Northern hemisphere at midday — **A**, **B**, **C** or **D**? ....

The Earth and Beyond Mini-Exam

(iii) Explain your answer to (ii), using the diagram below to help.

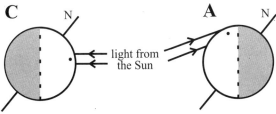

....

....

....

(iv) What **other** effect is due to the position of the Earth in its orbit?
Explain your answer.

....

....

....

(d) Look back at the diagram at the beginning of question 3. The constellation of Orion is clearly
visible at night in the northern hemisphere, but only during the winter. Explain why.

....

....

(e) One of the objects in Orion, called the **Orion Nebula**, is not really a star.
It looks dim and blurred compared to the stars in the constellation.
Suggest what the Orion Nebula might be. Explain your answer.

....

....

The Earth and Beyond Mini-Exam

4   The Solar System is held together by the gravity of the Sun.

(a)   What is gravity?

....

(b)   Explain why it is the gravity of the Sun that holds the Solar System together.

....

....

(c)   Comets are giant, frozen masses that travel right
to the edges of the Solar System.
The diagram on the right shows the orbit of
one comet around the Sun.

(i)   What term is used to describe the **shape** of the comet's orbit?

....

(ii)   The comet is much smaller than any of the planets in the Solar System.
Suggest why its orbit is much larger.

....

....

(iii)   What will happen to the gravity affecting the comet as it gets closer to the Sun?
Explain your answer.

....

....

(d)   The Earth's orbit gives it just the right amount of heat from the Sun to sustain life.

(i)   Suggest which **two** planets orbit just outside this area.

1 ....   2 ....

(ii)   Suggest why life cannot be sustained on these two planets.

Planet 1 ....

Planet 2 ....

Forms of Energy

1 Different forms of energy are needed for different activities.

(a) Write down the **main** form of energy being demonstrated in each of the diagrams below.

(i) ....

(iii) ....

(ii) Supercell ....

(iv) ....

(b) Draw lines to join each form of energy on the left to the **most appropriate** example on the right.

chemical	digging the garden
sound	the energy flowing from a power station
gravitational potential	a bar of chocolate
kinetic	loud music on the radio
electrical	a skydiver stepping out of an aeroplane

2 Jimmy is sitting by a fire to keep warm.

(a) He says that there's no heat in his body. Is he right? Explain your answer.

....

....

(b) He says that the temperature of the fire is flowing into his body.
Is he right? Explain your answer.

....

....

Energy Transformations

1   An electric toothbrush has a rechargeable battery.

(a) Tick the correct box to show the energy transformation
     taking place as the battery is recharged.

☐ kinetic to sound   ☐ electrical to chemical

☐ chemical to electrical   ☐ heat to kinetic

(b) What **useful** energy transformation takes place when the brush is used?
     Tick the correct box.

☐ electrical to kinetic to sound   ☐ electrical to chemical to kinetic

☐ chemical to electrical to kinetic   ☐ chemical to sound to kinetic

2   Write down the energy transformations happening in the pictures below.
     (Note that **one** form of energy can be transferred to become **more than one** form.)

(a)

....

(b)

....

(c)

....

(d)

....

Transfer of Energy

1   Oliver heats one end of a piece of copper wire in a Bunsen burner flame.
     The other end of the wire soon gets hot as well.

  (a) Why is heat energy transferred along the wire?

     ....

  (b) What process transfers the heat energy along the wire?

     ....

  (c) Describe how the heat energy is transferred along the wire.

     ....

     ....

     ....

2   Gliders make use of rising currents of warm air called **thermals**.

  (a) Name the process by which thermals transfer heat energy.

     ....

  (b) Why are there no thermals in a vacuum such as outer space?

     ....

     ....

3   Tankers visit farms every day to collect milk. The milk must be kept cold to help it stay fresh.

  (a) Describe how the heat of the Sun could be transferred to the milk inside the tankers.

     ....

     ....

  (b) Suggest why milk tankers are usually a shiny silver colour.

     ....

     ....

Energy Resources

1   **Light** from the Sun provides us with energy resources in the form of **fossil fuels** and **biomass**.

(a)   Explain why plants are important in the production of these energy resources.

....

....

(b)   Describe how fossil fuels are formed.

....

....

....

(c)   Name **two** types of biomass we use as energy resources.

1 ....   2 ....

(d)   For **one** of the energy resources named in (c), describe the chain of energy transformations that converts the light energy from the Sun into a form that we use.

....

....

2   Winds are an energy resource. Wind turbines can be used to generate electricity.

(a)   (i)   What form of energy is the energy of wind?

....

(ii)   Using the diagram below, explain how the energy of the Sun causes winds.

....

....

warm air

cooler air

warm land

Sea cool

....

....

(b)   What other energy resource results from winds?

....

Generating Electricity

1   Our electricity is generated in power stations.

(a) Name **three** fuels that are burnt in power stations.

1 ....   2 ....   3 ....

(b) Explain why petrol is **not** burnt in power stations.

....

(c) Give **two** important uses of electricity within the home.

1 ....   2 ....

2   The three main parts of a power station are shown below.

A   **B**   **C**

(a) Write down the **letters** of the parts in the order that they are used to generate electricity.
     Write the **name** of the part next to each letter.

1 **Letter** ....   **Name** ....

2 **Letter** ....   **Name** ....

3 **Letter** ....   **Name** ....

(b) Describe how the parts convert the chemical energy in fuels
     into electrical energy we can use in our homes.

....

....

....

....

....

Generating Electricity

1   The amount of fossil fuels burnt can be reduced by **saving energy**
    and by using **renewable energy resources** instead.

(a) Explain why scientists warn that we should reduce the rate at which we are burning fossil fuels.

....

....

(b) Suggest **two** ways of saving energy.

1 ....

2 ....

(c) (i)   Name **three** renewable energy resources that could be used to replace fossil fuels.

1 ....

2 ....

3 ....

(ii) Explain why these resources are called **renewable** rather than **re-usable**.

....

....

2   Many calculators have a solar cell like the one in the picture.

(a) What energy transformation takes place in the calculator?

.... $\longrightarrow$ ....

(b) Write down **two** advantages of using a solar cell in a calculator.

1 ....

2 ....

(c) Give **one** disadvantage.

....

Conservation of Energy

1 Answer the following questions about energy.

(a) Gemma says that heat energy can be created by rubbing two sticks together really fast.
Is she correct? Explain your answer.

....

....

(b) Put a tick in the boxes next to the statements that are **true** below.

☐ **Energy is only useful when it's converted from one form into another.**

☐ **Output energy from machines is the same as input energy, but more useful.**

☐ **Energy is always useful.**

☐ **Machines convert input energy into useful output energy.**

(c) Gemma notices that the computer room at school is warmer and noisier
than the other classrooms. Explain why this might be, in terms of energy.

....

....

2 For each machine below, name the form of the energy input,
the useful form of energy output and the form in which energy is wasted.
(Note that more than one form of energy may be used or wasted.)

(a)   Energy input   ....

Useful energy output   ....

Wasted energy output   ....

(b)   Energy input   ....

Useful energy output   ....

Wasted energy output   ....

Conservation of Energy

1   Look at the pictures of the two light bulbs.
    The ordinary light bulb has an energy input of 100 joules per second.
    The energy saver light bulb has an energy input of 20 joules per second.
    Both bulbs give out the same amount of light energy per second.

    ordinary   energy saver
    light bulb   light bulb

    (a) Explain how it is possible that both bulbs can
         give out the same amount of light energy per second.

         ....

    (b) Suggest **two** advantages of using the energy saver bulbs instead of the ordinary bulbs.

         1 ....

         2 ....

2   A petrol-engined car, electric lawnmower and wind turbine all waste energy at different rates.

    (a) Calculate the following energy values for each device.

         (i)   For every 100 joules of energy input, the car wastes 75 joules.

               Useful energy = ... joules

         (ii) For every 80 joules of useful energy output, the lawnmower wastes 120 joules.

               Input energy = ... joules

         (iii) The wind turbine has an energy input of 400 joules and an energy output of 80 joules.

               Wasted energy = ... joules

    (b) What is the **useful** form of energy output by:

         (i)   both the car and the lawnmower?   ....

         (ii) the wind turbine?   ....

    (c) Which device is

         (i)   **most** wasteful of energy?   ....

         (ii) **least** wasteful of energy?   ....

    (d) Name **two** forms of energy wasted by all three devices.

         1 ....   2 ....

Energy Resources and Energy Mini-Exam

1   The diagram on the right shows a design for an oven.

steel shell

OUTSIDE
OF OVEN

INSIDE
OF OVEN

aluminium foil sheet

polystyrene

(a)   Steel is a good heat conductor.
Describe how heat energy is transferred through steel.

....

....

(b)   Polystyrene is **not** a good heat conductor. Suggest why it is used in the oven.

....

....

(c)   Aluminium foil is shiny and smooth. Suggest why it is used in the oven.

....

2   The picture shows the inside of an electric kettle.

water

element

(a)   What energy transformation takes place in the **element**
when the kettle is switched on?

....

(b)   (i)   The water in the kettle already has some energy. Explain this statement.

....

(ii)   Explain why the water gains more energy from the element.

....

(c)   (i)   Name the process by which energy is transferred through the water.

....

(ii)   Explain why the element is placed at the **bottom** of the kettle.
Use the word 'convection' in your answer.

....

....

Energy Resources and Energy Mini-Exam

3   Agnes is using a food mixer to make cake mix.

(a) The useful energy output of the food mixer is less than the electrical energy input.
     Agnes states that "some of the energy disappears."

(i)   Explain why Agnes's statement is incorrect.

     ....

     ....

(ii) The diagram below shows the energy transformations that happen in the food mixer.
      Fill in the missing information.

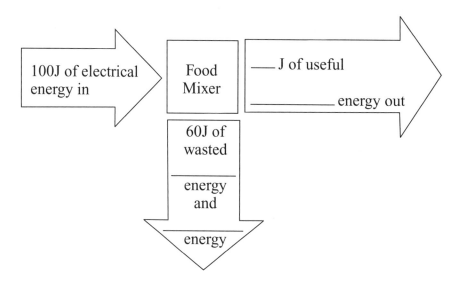

(b) The electricity grid that the food mixer is connected to is supplied by a
     coal-fired power station and a **hydroelectric** power station.

     A simplified diagram of the hydroelectric power station is shown below.
     As the water flows downhill, it spins a turbine. The turbine is connected to a generator.

Energy Resources and Energy Mini-Exam

Fill in the gaps in the following sentences to show the **useful**
energy transformations that take place at the hydroelectric power station.

The .... **energy of the water is**

converted to .... **energy as**

the water flows downhill.

The .... **energy is converted to**

.... **energy in the generator.**

(c) The electrical energy generated in both the coal-fired power station and the
hydroelectric power station originally comes from the Sun.

(i) Explain how the Sun provides the energy in the
coal burnt in the coal-fired power station.

....

....

(ii) Suggest how the Sun provides the energy that is converted
into electrical energy in the hydroelectric power station.

....

(d) The turbines used in both power stations waste some energy.

(i) Name **one** form of energy wasted in a turbine.

....

(ii) Reducing the energy wasted in the turbines is one way of saving our energy resources.
Explain why this is particularly important in the coal-fired power station.

....

....

....

Energy Resources and Energy Mini-Exam

4   John is loading a lorry with large stone blocks from a pile on the ground.

Large block of stone

John lifting stone

Stone on back of lorry

Not to scale

(a)   As he lifts a block, energy is transferred from John to the block.

    (i)   What form is the energy in before John lifts the block?

        ....

    (ii)   Where is the energy stored before John lifts the block?

        ....

(b)   (i)   As John lifts a block off the ground and up to the height of the lorry, the block has energy in **two** different forms. What are they?

        1   ....

        2   ....

    (ii)   The energy is stored in the block when it is on the back of the lorry. What form is the energy in?

        ....

(c)   One of the blocks is placed badly on the lorry, and falls off.

    (i)   What energy transformation takes place as the block falls?

        ....

    (ii)   What energy transformation takes place when the block hits the ground?

        ....